■SCHOLASTIC

# Do The Math™

Created by
**Marilyn Burns**

 # Addition & Subtraction Ⓑ

## Subtraction with numbers up to 100

## WorkSpace

Copyright © 2008 by Scholastic Inc.

All rights reserved.          Published by Scholastic Inc.          Printed in the U.S.A.

ISBN-13: 978-0-545-00999-7
ISBN-10: 0-545-00999-5

SCHOLASTIC, DO THE MATH, and associated logos and designs are trademarks and/or registered trademarks of Scholastic Inc.

11 12 13          40          16  15  14  13

v.B

# Subtract from 10s

DIRECTIONS

**1**

Number __4__

10 − __4__ = ___

20 − __4__ = ___

30 − __4__ = ___

40 − __4__ = ___

Write the number in the
first blank of each equation.

**2**

10 − __4__ = __6__

20 − __4__ = __16__

30 − __4__ = __26__

40 − __4__ = __36__

Use the pattern to complete the equations.
You may check your answers
with the 1 to 100 chart.

---

**① Number __5__**

10 − __5__ = __5__

20 − __5__ = __15__

30 − __5__ = __25__ ✓

40 − __5__ = __35__

50 − __5__ = __45__

**② Number __7__**

10 − __7__ = __10__

20 − __7__ = __13__

40 − __7__ = __34__

60 − __7__ = __53__

80 − __7__ = __73__

**③ Number __9__**

10 − __9__ = __19__

30 − __9__ = __23__

50 − __9__ = __43__

70 − __9__ = __69__

90 − __9__ = __83__

**④ Number __6__**

10 − __6__ = __6__

60 − __6__ = __53__

70 − __6__ = __53__

80 − __6__ = __73__

90 − __6__ = __88__

---

Lesson 1

**Home Note:** Your child uses patterns to subtract one-digit numbers from 10s.

# 1 to 100 Chart

| 1 | 2 | 3 | 4 | 5 | 6 | 7 | 8 | 9 | 10 |
|---|---|---|---|---|---|---|---|---|---|
| 11 | 12 | 13 | 14 | 15 | 16 | 17 | 18 | 19 | 20 |
| 21 | 22 | 23 | 24 | 25 | 26 | 27 | 28 | 29 | 30 |
| 31 | 32 | 33 | 34 | 35 | 36 | 37 | 38 | 39 | 40 |
| 41 | 42 | 43 | 44 | 45 | 46 | 47 | 48 | 49 | 50 |
| 51 | 52 | 53 | 54 | 55 | 56 | 57 | 58 | 59 | 60 |
| 61 | 62 | 63 | 64 | 65 | 66 | 67 | 68 | 69 | 70 |
| 71 | 72 | 73 | 74 | 75 | 76 | 77 | 78 | 79 | 80 |
| 81 | 82 | 83 | 84 | 85 | 86 | 87 | 88 | 89 | 90 |
| 91 | 92 | 93 | 94 | 95 | 96 | 97 | 98 | 99 | 100 |

**Home Note:** Your child uses patterns to subtract one-digit numbers from 10s.

# Add and Subtract with Open Number Lines

## DIRECTIONS

| | 1 | 2 |
|---|---|---|
| $8 - 3 =$ ___ | $\overset{-3}{\underset{5 \qquad 8}{\curvearrowleft}}$ <br> Draw an open number line to solve the problem. | $8 - 3 = 5$ <br> Write the equation for the problem. |

| Problem | Open Number Line | Equation |
|---|---|---|
| ① $5 + 4 = \underline{9}$ | $5 \overset{4}{+} 9$ | $5+4=9$ |
| ② $9 - 4 = \underline{7}$ | $4 \frown 9 = 7$ | $9-4=7$ |
| ③ $3 + 6 = \underline{9}$ | $3 \frown 6 = 9$ | $3+6=9$ |
| ④ $9 - 6 = \underline{3}$ | $6 \frown 9 = 3$ | $9-6=3$ |
| ⑤ $1 + 8 = \underline{9}$ | $1 + 8 = 9$ | $1+8=9$ |
| ⑥ $9 - 8 = \underline{1}$ | $8 = 9 = 1$ | $9 - 8 = 1$ |
| ⑦ $2 + 5 = \underline{7}$ | $2 + 5 = 7$ | $2 + 5 = 7$ |
| ⑧ $7 - 5 = \underline{2}$ | $7 \frown 5 = 2$ | $7-5=2$ |

Lesson 2

**Home Note:** Your child adds and subtracts numbers up to 10 by drawing open number lines and writing equations.

# Subtract with Open Number Lines and Equations

| | **1** | **2** | **3** |
|---|---|---|---|
| $64 - 6 = \underline{\quad}$ | $-2 \quad -4$<br>$58 \quad 60 \qquad 64$<br><br>Draw an open number line to solve the problem. | $64 - 4 = 60$<br>$60 - 2 = 58$<br><br>Write equations to solve the problem. | $64 - 6 = \underline{58}$<br><br>Write the answer in the subtraction equation. |

| Problem | Open Number Line | Subtraction Equations |
|---|---|---|
| ① $75 - 8 = \underline{\quad}$ | $-3 \quad -5$<br>$67 \quad 70 \qquad 75$ | |
| ② $85 - 6 = \underline{\quad}$ | $-1 \quad -5$<br>$79 \quad 80 \qquad 85$ | |

**Home Note:** Your child solves subtraction problems by writing equations and drawing open number lines.

Lesson 3

5

# Solve Subtraction Problems

DIRECTIONS

| | | | |
|---|---|---|---|
| $64 - 6 =$ ___ | **1** $-2$  $-4$  58  60  64  Draw an open number line to solve the problem. | **2** $64 - 4 = 60$  $60 - 2 = 58$  Write equations to solve the problem. | **3** $64 - 6 =$ _58_  Write the answer in the subtraction equation. |

| Problem | Open Number Line | Subtraction Equations |
|---|---|---|
| ① $22 - 7 = 15$ | 5-  2-  15  20  22 | |
| ② $33 - 4 = 29$ | 1-  3-  29  30  33 | |
| ③ $55 - 9 = 45$ | 4  5-  45  50  55 | |
| ④ $21 - 8 = 18$ | 7-  1-  18  20  21 | |
| ⑤ $42 - 6 =$ ___ | 4-  2-  36  40  42 | |

Lesson 3

**Home Note:** Your child solves subtraction problems by writing equations and drawing open number lines.

# Practice Turns for Six Rolls

➤ Record open number lines and equations that your teacher demonstrates in class.

| **Roll 1** | Equation _____ |
| | Open Number Line |

| **Roll 2** | Equation _____ |
| | Open Number Line |

| **Roll 3** | Equation _____ |
| | Open Number Line |

| **Roll 4** | Equation _____ |
| | Open Number Line |

| **Roll 5** | Equation _____ |
| | Open Number Line |

| **Roll 6** | Equation _____ |
| | Open Number Line |

**Final Score** _____

**Home Note:** Your child records practice turns of a subtraction game.

# Game Rules for Six Rolls

**What you need**

- number cube (4–9)
- *WorkSpace* page 9

➤ **Players take turns, for 6 turns each. The starting number is 50.**

**1**

Player A rolls the number cube.

**2**

| Player A | |
|---|---|
| Roll 1 <br> 7 | Equation $50 - 7 = 43$ <br> Open Number Line <br>  |

Player A records the roll, subtracts it from 50
using an open number line, and writes the equation.

**3**

| Player A | |
|---|---|
| Roll 1 <br> 7 | Equation $50 - 7 = 43$ <br> Open Number Line |
| Roll 2 <br> 5 | Equation $43 - 5 = 38$ <br> Open Number Line <br>  |

The answer for each turn is the
starting number for the next turn.

➤ **The winner is the player whose final score is closer to 0.**

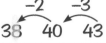 **Home Note:** Your child practices subtracting one-digit
numbers from two-digit numbers by playing a game.

# Six Rolls

| Player A | | Player B | |
|---|---|---|---|
| **Roll 1** ___ | Equation _____<br>Open Number Line | **Roll 1** ___ | Equation _____<br>Open Number Line |
| **Roll 2** ___ | Equation _____<br>Open Number Line | **Roll 2** ___ | Equation _____<br>Open Number Line |
| **Roll 3** ___ | Equation _____<br>Open Number Line | **Roll 3** ___ | Equation _____<br>Open Number Line |
| **Roll 4** ___ | Equation _____<br>Open Number Line | **Roll 4** ___ | Equation _____<br>Open Number Line |
| **Roll 5** ___ | Equation _____<br>Open Number Line | **Roll 5** ___ | Equation _____<br>Open Number Line |
| **Roll 6** ___ | Equation _____<br>Open Number Line | **Roll 6** ___ | Equation _____<br>Open Number Line |
| **Final Score** | _____ | **Final Score** | _____ |

**Home Note:** Your child practices subtracting one-digit numbers from two-digit numbers by playing a game.

# Game Rules for Get Close to Zero

**What you need**

- number cube (4–9)
- *WorkSpace* page 11

➤ **You play alone, taking as many turns as you can.**
**The starting number is 50.**

**1**

Roll the number cube.

**2**

| Roll 1 | Equation $50 - 8 = 42$ |
|---|---|
| 8 | Open Number Line |

Record your roll, subtract it from 50 using an open number line, and write the equation.

**3**

| Roll 1 | Equation $50 - 8 = 42$ |
|---|---|
| 8 | Open Number Line |
| Roll 2 | Equation $42 - 6 = 36$ |
| 6 | Open Number Line |

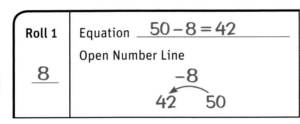

Roll the number cube again and subtract. The answer for each turn is the starting number for the next turn.

➤ **Continue until you get as close to 0 as you can.**

➤ **If you roll a number that would drop your score below 0, your game is over.**

**Home Note:** Your child practices subtracting one-digit numbers from two-digit numbers by playing a game.

# Get Close to Zero—Show What You Know

| | |
|---|---|
| **Roll 1** | Equation _____ |
| | Open Number Line |
| _____ | |

| | |
|---|---|
| **Roll 6** | Equation _____ |
| | Open Number Line |
| _____ | |

| | |
|---|---|
| **Roll 2** | Equation _____ |
| | Open Number Line |
| _____ | |

| | |
|---|---|
| **Roll 7** | Equation _____ |
| | Open Number Line |
| _____ | |

| | |
|---|---|
| **Roll 3** | Equation _____ |
| | Open Number Line |
| _____ | |

| | |
|---|---|
| **Roll 8** | Equation _____ |
| | Open Number Line |
| _____ | |

| | |
|---|---|
| **Roll 4** | Equation _____ |
| | Open Number Line |
| _____ | |

| | |
|---|---|
| **Roll 9** | Equation _____ |
| | Open Number Line |
| _____ | |

| | |
|---|---|
| **Roll 5** | Equation _____ |
| | Open Number Line |
| _____ | |

| | |
|---|---|
| **Roll 10** | Equation _____ |
| | Open Number Line |
| _____ | |

**Home Note:** Your child practices subtracting one-digit numbers from two-digit numbers by playing a game.

# Get Close to Zero

| Roll 1 | Equation _____ |
| | Open Number Line |
| _____ | |

| Roll 6 | Equation _____ |
| | Open Number Line |
| _____ | |

| Roll 2 | Equation _____ |
| | Open Number Line |
| _____ | |

| Roll 7 | Equation _____ |
| | Open Number Line |
| _____ | |

| Roll 3 | Equation _____ |
| | Open Number Line |
| _____ | |

| Roll 8 | Equation _____ |
| | Open Number Line |
| _____ | |

| Roll 4 | Equation _____ |
| | Open Number Line |
| _____ | |

| Roll 9 | Equation _____ |
| | Open Number Line |
| _____ | |

| Roll 5 | Equation _____ |
| | Open Number Line |
| _____ | |

| Roll 10 | Equation _____ |
| | Open Number Line |
| _____ | |

**Home Note:** Your child practices subtracting one-digit
numbers from two-digit numbers by playing a game.

# Add and Subtract 10 Using Open Number Lines

| | 1 | 2 |
|---|---|---|
| 33 + 10 = ____ | $+10$ <br> 33 → 43 <br> Draw an open number line. <br> • Where do I start? <br> • What jumps do I make? <br> • Where do I end up? | 33 + 10 = 43 <br><br> Write an equation. |

| Problem | Open Number Line | Equation |
|---|---|---|
| ① 34 + 10 = ____ | $+10$ <br> 34 → 44 | 34 + 10 = 44 |
| ② 26 + 10 = ____ | $+10$ <br> 26 → 36 | 26 + 10 = 36 |
| ③ 63 − 10 = ____ | $-10$ <br> 63 → 53 | 63 − 10 = 53 |
| ④ 49 − 10 = ____ | $-10$ <br> 49 → 39 | $-10$ <br> 49 → 39 |

**Home Note:** Your child subtracts 10 from two-digit numbers by drawing open number lines and writing equations.

# Add and Subtract 10 Using Open Number Lines

| | | |
|---|---|---|
| 33 + 10 = ____ | **1** $$33 \xrightarrow{+10} 43$$ Draw an open number line. • Where do I start? • What jumps do I make? • Where do I end up? | **2** 33 + 10 = 43 Write an equation. |

| Problem | Open Number Line | Equation |
|---|---|---|
| ① 70 − 10 = ____ | $$60 \xleftarrow{-10} 70$$ | 70 − 10 = 60 |
| ② 45 − 10 = ____ | 45 $\xrightarrow{-10}$ 35 |  |
| ③ 43 + 10 = ____ | 43 $\xrightarrow{-10}$ 33 | |
| ④ 27 − 10 = ____ | 27 $\xrightarrow{-10}$ 17 | |
| ⑤ 18 + 10 = ____ | 18 $\xrightarrow{+10}$ 8 | |
| ⑥ 38 − 10 = ____ | 38 $\xrightarrow{+10}$ 28 | |

**Home Note:** Your child solves problems by adding and subtracting 10.

# Record Two Open Number Lines For One Problem

## DIRECTIONS

**1**
$$60 - 40$$
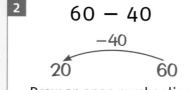
$-10$ $-10$ $-10$ $-10$
20  30  40  50  60
Draw an open number line with more than one jump.

**2**
$$60 - 40$$
$-40$
20              60
Draw an open number line with one jump.

**3**
$$60 - 40 = 20$$
Write a subtraction equation.

---

**①** $37 - 20$

| Open number line with more than one jump | Open number line with one jump |
|---|---|
| 37 $-20$ 17 | 37 $-20$ 17 |

Equation

---

**②** $78 - 40$

| Open number line with more than one jump | Open number line with one jump |
|---|---|
| 78 $-40$ 58  | 78 $-40$ 58  |

Equation

---

**Home Note:** Your child records two open number lines and an equation to subtract a ten from a two-digit number.

# Record Two Open Number Lines
# For One Problem

DIRECTIONS

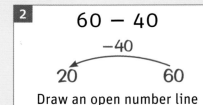

**1**    60 − 40

−10 −10 −10 −10

20   30   40   50   60

Draw an open number line
with more than one jump.

**2**    60 − 40

−40

20        60

Draw an open number line
with one jump.

**3**

60 − 40 = 20

Write a subtraction
equation.

---

**①**   63 − 30

| Open number line with more than one jump | Open number line with one jump |
|---|---|
| | |

Equation

**②**   45 − 20

| Open number line with more than one jump | Open number line with one jump |
|---|---|
| | |

Equation

**③**   90 − 50

| Open number line with more than one jump | Open number line with one jump |
|---|---|
| | |

Equation

**Home Note:** Your child records two open number lines and
an equation to subtract a ten from a two-digit number.

# Get Close to Zero with Six Rolls— Practice Game

| Roll 1 ____ | Equation _____<br>Open Number Line |
|---|---|
| Roll 2 ____ | Equation _____<br>Open Number Line |
| Roll 3 ____ | Equation _____<br>Open Number Line |
| Roll 4 ____ | Equation _____<br>Open Number Line |
| Roll 5 ____ | Equation _____<br>Open Number Line |
| Roll 6 ____ | Equation _____<br>Open Number Line |

Final Score _____

**Home Note:** Your child practices subtracting ones and tens from two-digit numbers by playing a game.

# Game Rules for Get Close to Zero with Six Rolls

**What you need**

- number cube (1–6)
- *WorkSpace* page 19

➤ **Players take turns, for 6 turns each.**

**1**

Player A rolls the number cube.

**2**

| Player A | |
|---|---|
| **Roll 1** <br> 4 | Equation  $100 - 40 = 60$ <br><br> Open Number Line <br> $-40$ <br> 60 ⌒ 100 |

Player A records the roll, writes the number as
ones or tens, then subtracts it from 100 using an
open number line, and writes the equation.

**3**

| Player A | |
|---|---|
| **Roll 1** <br> 4 | Equation  $100 - 40 = 60$ <br><br> Open Number Line <br> $-40$ <br> 60 ⌒ 100 |
| **Roll 2** <br> 5 | Equation  $60 - 5 = 55$ <br><br> Open Number Line <br> $-5$ <br> 55 ⌒ 60 |

The answer for each turn is the
starting number for the next turn.

➤ **The winner is the player whose final score is closer to,
but not less than, 0.**

**Home Note:** Your child practices subtracting ones
and tens from two-digit numbers by playing a game.

# Get Close to Zero with Six Rolls

| Player A | | Player B | |
|---|---|---|---|
| **Roll 1** ____ | Equation _____<br>Open Number Line | **Roll 1** ____ | Equation _____<br>Open Number Line |
| **Roll 2** ____ | Equation _____<br>Open Number Line | **Roll 2** ____ | Equation _____<br>Open Number Line |
| **Roll 3** ____ | Equation _____<br>Open Number Line | **Roll 3** ____ | Equation _____<br>Open Number Line |
| **Roll 4** ____ | Equation _____<br>Open Number Line | **Roll 4** ____ | Equation _____<br>Open Number Line |
| **Roll 5** ____ | Equation _____<br>Open Number Line | **Roll 5** ____ | Equation _____<br>Open Number Line |
| **Roll 6** ____ | Equation _____<br>Open Number Line | **Roll 6** ____ | Equation _____<br>Open Number Line |
| **Final Score** _____ | | **Final Score** _____ | |

**Home Note:** Your child practices subtracting ones and tens from two-digit numbers by playing a game.

Lesson 8

# Get Close to Zero with Six Rolls

| Player A | | Player B | |
|---|---|---|---|
| **Roll 1** \_\_\_\_ | Equation _____ <br> Open Number Line | **Roll 1** \_\_\_\_ | Equation _____ <br> Open Number Line |
| **Roll 2** \_\_\_\_ | Equation _____ <br> Open Number Line | **Roll 2** \_\_\_\_ | Equation _____ <br> Open Number Line |
| **Roll 3** \_\_\_\_ | Equation _____ <br> Open Number Line | **Roll 3** \_\_\_\_ | Equation _____ <br> Open Number Line |
| **Roll 4** \_\_\_\_ | Equation _____ <br> Open Number Line | **Roll 4** \_\_\_\_ | Equation _____ <br> Open Number Line |
| **Roll 5** \_\_\_\_ | Equation _____ <br> Open Number Line | **Roll 5** \_\_\_\_ | Equation _____ <br> Open Number Line |
| **Roll 6** \_\_\_\_ | Equation _____ <br> Open Number Line | **Roll 6** \_\_\_\_ | Equation _____ <br> Open Number Line |
| **Final Score** _____ | | **Final Score** _____ | |

**Home Note:** Your child practices subtracting ones and tens from two-digit numbers by playing a game.

# Show What You Know

DIRECTIONS

| | **1** | **2** |
|---|---|---|
| $72 - 6 =$ ____ | −4  −2<br>66  70  72<br>Draw an open number line. | $72 - 6 = 66$<br>Write an equation. |

| Problem | Open Number Line | Equation |
|---|---|---|
| ① $44 - 10 =$ ____ | | |
| ② $81 - 30 =$ ____ | | |
| ③ $61 - 4 =$ ____ | | |
| ④ $33 - 9 =$ ____ | | |
| ⑤ $85 - 8 =$ ____ | | |
| ⑥ $48 - 20 =$ ____ | | |
| ⑦ $76 - 60 =$ ____ | | |
| ⑧ $92 - 3 =$ ____ | | |

**Home Note:** Your child practices subtracting ones and tens from two-digit numbers by drawing open number lines and writing equations.

# Get Close to Zero with Six Rolls

| Player A | | Player B | |
|---|---|---|---|
| **Roll 1** ___ | Equation _____<br>Open Number Line | **Roll 1** ___ | Equation _____<br>Open Number Line |
| **Roll 2** ___ | Equation _____<br>Open Number Line | **Roll 2** ___ | Equation _____<br>Open Number Line |
| **Roll 3** ___ | Equation _____<br>Open Number Line | **Roll 3** ___ | Equation _____<br>Open Number Line |
| **Roll 4** ___ | Equation _____<br>Open Number Line | **Roll 4** ___ | Equation _____<br>Open Number Line |
| **Roll 5** ___ | Equation _____<br>Open Number Line | **Roll 5** ___ | Equation _____<br>Open Number Line |
| **Roll 6** ___ | Equation _____<br>Open Number Line | **Roll 6** ___ | Equation _____<br>Open Number Line |
| **Final Score** | _____ | **Final Score** | _____ |

**Home Note:** Your child practices subtracting ones and tens from two-digit numbers by playing a game.

# Split a Number to Subtract

I had $75.
I spent $16.

How much do
I have left?

**1**

$75 - 16 = \underline{\phantom{00}}$

Write the problem.

**2**

$$\overset{-1}{\underset{59\ \ 60}{\curvearrowleft}} \quad \overset{-5}{\underset{65}{\curvearrowleft}} \quad \overset{-10}{\underset{75}{\curvearrowleft}}$$

Draw an open number line.
• Where do I start?
• What jumps do I make?
• Where do I end up?

**3**

$75 - 16 = 59$

Write an equation.

| | Problem | Open Number Line | Equation |
|---|---|---|---|
| I had $74. <br> I spent $19. <br><br> How much do <br> I have left? | | | |

**Home Note:** Your child uses splitting to subtract
two-digit numbers from two-digit numbers.

# Solve Subtraction Word Problems

DIRECTIONS

I had $75.
I spent $16.

How much do
I have left?

**1**

$75 - 16 =$ ___

Write the problem.

**2**

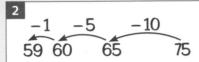

Draw an open number line.
• Where do I start?
• What jumps do I make?
• Where do I end up?

**3**

$75 - 16 = 59$

Write an equation.

| | Problem | Open Number Line | Equation |
|---|---|---|---|
| ① I had $60.<br>I spent $26.<br><br>How much do<br>I have left? | | | |
| ② I had $63.<br>I spent $39.<br><br>How much do<br>I have left? | | | |
| ③ I had $52.<br>I spent $44.<br><br>How much do<br>I have left? | | | |
| ④ I had $94.<br>I spent $16.<br><br>How much do<br>I have left? | | | |

**Home Note:** Your child uses splitting to subtract
two-digit numbers from two-digit numbers.

# Get Close to Zero with Two Cubes Practice Game

| Roll | Two-Digit Number | Open Number Line | Equation |
|---|---|---|---|
| **EXAMPLE** $\frac{5}{1}$ | 51 | $-1$ $\quad$ $-50$ $\quad$ 49 $\;$ 50 $\qquad$ 100 | $100 - 51 = 49$ |
| ① ___ ___ | | | |
| ② ___ ___ | | | |
| ③ ___ ___ | | | |
| ④ ___ ___ | | | |
| ⑤ ___ ___ | | | |
| ⑥ ___ ___ | | | |
| ⑦ ___ ___ | | | |
| ⑧ ___ ___ | | | |

**Home Note:** Your child practices subtracting two-digit numbers by playing a game.

# Games Rules for Get Close to Zero with Two Cubes

HOW TO PLAY

**What you need**

- two number cubes (1–6)
- *WorkSpace* page 27

➤ **Play alone. The starting number is 100.**

**1**

| Roll | Two-Digit Number |
|------|------------------|
| 5 1  | 51               |

Roll the number cubes. Decide which two-digit number to make. Record the number.

**2**

| Open Number Line |
|------------------|

$$-1 \quad\quad -50$$
$$49 \;\; 50 \quad\quad\quad 100$$

Subtract the number from your score using an open number line.

**3**

| Equation |
|----------|

$$100 - 51 = 49$$

Write a subtraction equation. The answer is your score.

➤ **Continue until you get to 0 or you roll two numbers that would drop the answer below 0. The answer for each turn is the starting number for the next turn.**

Lesson 12

**Home Note:** Your child practices subtracting two-digit numbers by playing a game.

# Get Close to Zero with Two Cubes

| Roll | Two-Digit Number | Open Number Line | Equation |
|------|------------------|------------------|----------|
| EXAMPLE $\frac{5}{1}$ | 51 | −1  −50<br>49 50          100 | $100 - 51 = 49$ |
| ① ___ ___ | | | |
| ② ___ ___ | | | |
| ③ ___ ___ | | | |
| ④ ___ ___ | | | |
| ⑤ ___ ___ | | | |
| ⑥ ___ ___ | | | |
| ⑦ ___ ___ | | | |
| ⑧ ___ ___ | | | |

**Home Note:** Your child practices subtracting two-digit numbers by playing a game.

Lesson 12

# Get Close to Zero with Two Cubes

| Roll | Two-Digit Number | Open Number Line | Equation |
|------|------------------|------------------|----------|
| **EXAMPLE** $\frac{5}{1}$ | 51 | $-1$  $-50$ <br> 49 50        100 | $100 - 51 = 49$ |
| ① __ __ | | | |
| ② __ __ | | | |
| ③ __ __ | | | |
| ④ __ __ | | | |
| ⑤ __ __ | | | |
| ⑥ __ __ | | | |
| ⑦ __ __ | | | |
| ⑧ __ __ | | | |

**Home Note:** Your child practices subtracting two-digit numbers by playing a game.

# How Alexander Spent and Lost His Money

➤ Write the amount of money that Alexander spent or lost at each part of the story.

| How Alexander Spent or Lost His Money | Amount (¢) |
|---|---|
| Bubblegum | |
| Lost three bets | |
| Rented a snake | |
| Fined for bad words | |
| Lost money | |
| Brother's candy bar | |
| Magic trick | |
| Fined for kicking | |
| Garage sale | |
| **TOTAL** | |

**Home Note:** Your child records the amounts of money spent or lost by a character in a story.

# How Much Money Did Alexander Have Left?

## DIRECTIONS

➤ Write the problem. Draw an open number line to show how much money Alexander had left each time he spent or lost money.

➤ Write the equation for the problem.

| How Alexander Spent or Lost His Money | Amount | Open Number Line | Equation |
|---|---|---|---|
| Bubblegum<br>$100 - 15 = $ ___ | 15¢ | $-5$   $-10$<br>85  90    100 | **EXAMPLE**<br>$100 - 15 = 85$ |
| Lost three bets | 15¢ | | |
| Rented a snake | 12¢ | | |
| Fined for bad words | 10¢ | | |
| Lost money | 8¢ | | |
| Brother's candy bar | 11¢ | | |
| Magic trick | 4¢ | | |
| Fined for kicking | 5¢ | | |
| Garage sale | 20¢ | | |

**Home Note:** Your child solves subtraction word problems based on the amounts of money spent or lost by a character in a story.

# Show What You Know

**1** Suppose Alexander starts with $100.

| Buys shoes<br>100 − 25 = ___ | $25 |

Write the problem.

**2**

$$-5 \qquad -20$$
75   80        100

Draw an open number line starting with the amount Alexander has left.

**3**

$$100 - 25 = 75$$

Write a subtraction equation.

| How Alexander Spent His Money | Amount | Open Number Line | Equation |
|---|---|---|---|
| Buys shoes<br>100 − 25 = ___ | $25 | −5  −20<br>75  80      100 | EXAMPLE<br>$100 - 25 = 75$ |
| Buys flowers | $6 | | |
| Buys movie tickets | $18 | | |
| Buys snake food | $9 | | |
| Buys a walkie-talkie | $35 | | |
| Gives to a food bank | $7 | | |

**Home Note:** Your child solves subtraction word problems based on amounts of money spent by a character in a story.

# Get Close to Zero with Two Cubes

| Roll | Two-Digit Number | Open Number Line | Equation |
|---|---|---|---|
| **EXAMPLE** 5 / 1 | 51 | −1   −50<br>49  50      100 | $100 - 51 = 49$ |
| ① __ __ | | | |
| ② __ __ | | | |
| ③ __ __ | | | |
| ④ __ __ | | | |
| ⑤ __ __ | | | |
| ⑥ __ __ | | | |
| ⑦ __ __ | | | |
| ⑧ __ __ | | | |

**Home Note:** Your child practices subtracting two-digit numbers by playing a game.

# Comparing Problems

**1**

Alexander's team scored _50_ points.

Nicky's team scored _60_ points.

**What is the difference between the scores?**

(50, 60)

Read the problem using the pair of numbers.

**2**

$$+10$$
50    60

or

$$-10$$
50    60

Draw an open number line.

**3**

50 + _10_ = 60

or

60 − _10_ = 50

Write an equation.

**4**

10

Write the difference.

---

Alexander's team scored _____ points.

Nicky's team scored _____ points.

**What is the difference between the scores?**

| Pair of Numbers | Open Number Line | Equation | Difference |
|---|---|---|---|
| ① (51, 52) | | | |
| ② (70, 80) | | | |
| ③ (64, 74) | | | |

**Home Note:** Your child solves comparing subtraction problems by drawing open number lines and writing equations.

Lesson 16

33

# Comparing Problems

DIRECTIONS

**1**

Alexander is 51 inches tall.

Nicholas is 63 inches tall.

What is the difference between their heights?

Read the problem.

**2**

$$51 \xrightarrow{+10} 61 \xrightarrow{+2} 63$$

or

$$51 \; 53 \xleftarrow{-2} \xleftarrow{-10} 63$$

Draw an open number line.

**3**

$51 + \underline{\;12\;} = 63$

or

$63 - \underline{\;12\;} = 51$

Write an equation.

**4**

12

Write the difference.

| Problem | Open Number Line | Equation | Difference |
|---|---|---|---|
| Alexander is 10 years old. His grandmother is 62 years old. What is the difference between their ages? | | | |
| Alexander weighs 64 pounds. His brother Anthony weighs 85 pounds. How much heavier is Anthony than Alexander? | | | |
| Alexander has 67 stamps. Nicky has 37 stamps. How many fewer stamps does Nicky have than Alexander? | | | |
| A garter snake is 11 inches long. A boa constrictor is 20 inches long. How much longer is the boa constrictor than the garter snake? | | | |

**Home Note:** Your child solves comparing subtraction problems by drawing open number lines and writing equations.

# What's the Question? What's the Answer?

➤ Write a question for each problem.
➤ Draw an open number line to solve the problem.
➤ Write the equation and difference.

**(1)** My dog weighs 44 pounds.
My cat weighs 12 pounds.

_____?

| Open Number Line | Equation | Difference |
|---|---|---|
| | | |

**(2)** The high temperature today is 65 degrees.
The high temperature yesterday was 72 degrees.

_____?

| Open Number Line | Equation | Difference |
|---|---|---|
| | | |

**(3)** Use the following numbers to complete the problem: 21, 36.

The home team's score was _____.

The visiting team's score was _____.

_____?

| Open Number Line | Equation | Difference |
|---|---|---|
| | | |

**Home Note:** Your child solves comparing subtraction problems by drawing open number lines and writing equations.

Lesson 18

35

**④** **Use the following numbers to complete the problem: 56, 72.**

Perla is _____ inches tall.

Carla is _____ inches tall.

_____?

| Open Number Line | Equation | Difference |
|---|---|---|
| | | |

**⑤** **Write your own comparing problem about money.**

My numbers are _____, _____.

_____

_____

_____

_____?

| Open Number Line | Equation | Difference |
|---|---|---|
| | | |

**Home Note:** Your child writes comparing word problems and solves them.

# Comparing or Take-Away

**DIRECTIONS**

➤ Determine whether each problem is a comparing problem or a take-away problem.

➤ Circle *Comparing* or *Take-away.*

| Problem | Kind of Problem |
|---|---|
| **EXAMPLE**<br><br>Lara collected 42 cans.<br>Ramon collected 58 cans.<br><br>How many more cans did Ramon collect than Lara? | (Comparing)    Take-away |
| ① I baked 60 cookies.<br>I brought 30 of them to school for a party.<br><br>How many cookies did I leave at home? | Comparing    Take-away |
| ② It was 63 degrees in San Francisco.<br>It was 90 degrees in New York.<br><br>How much cooler was it in San Francisco than in New York? | Comparing    Take-away |
| ③ My friend scored 16 points in a basketball game.<br>I scored 10 points.<br><br>How many more points did my friend score than I? | Comparing    Take-away |
| ④ My brother collected 56 baseball cards.<br>He gave 25 of them to me.<br><br>How many baseball cards does he have left? | Comparing    Take-away |

**Home Note:** Your child determines whether subtraction problems are comparing or take-away problems.

# Solve Comparing and Take-Away Problems

**1**
Laura collected 42 cans.
Ramon collected 58 cans.

How many more cans did Ramon collect than Laura?

(Comparing)    Take-away

Read the problem. Circle Comparing or Take-away.

**2**
$$\overset{+10}{42 \longrightarrow} \overset{+6}{52 \longrightarrow 58}$$
or
$$\overset{-6}{42 \longleftarrow 48} \overset{-10}{\longleftarrow 58}$$

Draw an open number line.

**3**
$42 + \underline{16} = 58$

or

$58 - \underline{16} = 42$

Write an equation.

**4**

16

Write the difference.

---

**(1)** Brian has a box of 24 colored pencils.
Rosa has a box of 36 colored pencils.

How many more pencils does Rosa have than Brian?

**Comparing        Take-away**

| Open Number Line | Equation | Difference |
|---|---|---|
|  |  |  |

---

**(2)** Aneesa had $84.
She spent $62 on a camera.

How much money does she have left?

**Comparing        Take-away**

| Open Number Line | Equation | Difference |
|---|---|---|
|  |  |  |

---

**Home Note:** Your child solves comparing and take-away subtraction problems.

**3** Drivers can drive 65 miles per hour on a highway.
They can drive 25 miles per hour near a school.

How much faster can they drive on the highway than near the school?

**Comparing     Take-away**

| Open Number Line | Equation | Difference |
|---|---|---|
|  |  |  |

**4** Miguel has $32.
His brother has $51.

How much less money does Miguel have than his brother?

**Comparing     Take-away**

| Open Number Line | Equation | Difference |
|---|---|---|
|  |  |  |

**Home Note:** Your child solves comparing and take-away subtraction problems.

# Show What You Know

➤ Read the problem. Circle *Comparing* or *Take-away*.

➤ Draw an open number line.

➤ Write the equation.

➤ Write the difference.

---

**1** Christina had a box of 60 crayons.
Mario had a box of 48 crayons.

How many more crayons did Christina have than Mario?

**Comparing**      **Take-away**

| Open Number Line | Equation | Difference |
|---|---|---|
| | | |

---

**2** Henry had $32.
He spent $15 on a video.

How much money did he have left?

**Comparing**      **Take-away**

| Open Number Line | Equation | Difference |
|---|---|---|
| | | |

---

**Home Note:** Your child writes and solves comparing and take-away subtraction problems.

**③** Donna found 49¢ in her purse.
Tyrone found 72¢ in his pocket.

How much more money did Tyrone find than Donna?

**Comparing        Take-away**

| Open Number Line | Equation | Difference |
|---|---|---|
|  |  |  |

**④** Write your own comparing or take-away problem using the following numbers of jellybeans: 35, 50.

_____

_____

_____

**Comparing        Take-away**

| Open Number Line | Equation | Difference |
|---|---|---|
|  |  |  |

**⑤** Write your own comparing or take-away problem using the following amounts of money: $13, $47.

_____

_____

_____

**Comparing        Take-away**

| Open Number Line | Equation | Difference |
|---|---|---|
|  |  |  |

**Home Note:** Your child writes and solves comparing and take-away subtraction problems.

# Get Close to Zero with Two Cubes

| Roll | Two-Digit Number | Open Number Line | Equation |
|---|---|---|---|
| EXAMPLE $\frac{5}{1}$ | 51 | −1 −50 49 50 100 | 100 − 51 = 49 |
| ① __ __ | | | |
| ② __ __ | | | |
| ③ __ __ | | | |
| ④ __ __ | | | |
| ⑤ __ __ | | | |
| ⑥ __ __ | | | |
| ⑦ __ __ | | | |
| ⑧ __ __ | | | |

**Home Note:** Your child practices subtracting two-digit numbers by playing a game.

# Dollar Signs in One Minute

## DIRECTIONS

**1**

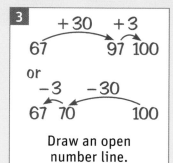

Draw dollar signs for one minute.

**2**

I drew _67_ dollar signs.

I need _33_ more to make 100.

Complete the sentences.

**3**

$$\overset{+30}{\underset{67}{\frown}} \overset{+3}{\underset{97\ 100}{\frown}}$$

or

$$\overset{-3}{\underset{67\ 70}{\frown}} \overset{-30}{\underset{100}{\frown}}$$

Draw an open number line.

**4**

$67 +$ _33_ $= 100$

or

$100 -$ _33_ $= 67$

Write an equation.

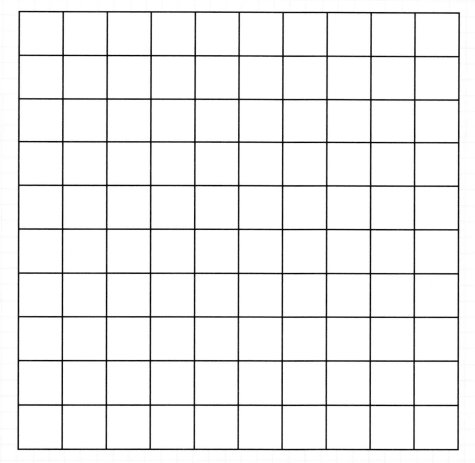

I drew _____ dollar signs.

I need _____ more to make 100.

| Open Number Line | Equation |
|---|---|
|  |  |

**Home Note:** Your child solves a part-part-whole subtraction problem by doing an activity.

# Dollar Signs in One Minute

## DIRECTIONS

**1**

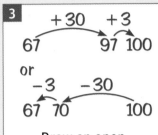

Draw dollar signs for one minute.

**2**

I drew __67__ dollar signs.

I need __33__ more to make 100.

Complete the sentences.

**3**

$$67 \xrightarrow{+30} 97 \xrightarrow{+3} 100$$

or

$$67 \; 70 \xleftarrow{-3} \xleftarrow{-30} 100$$

Draw an open number line.

**4**

$67 + \underline{33} = 100$

or

$100 - \underline{33} = 67$

Write an equation.

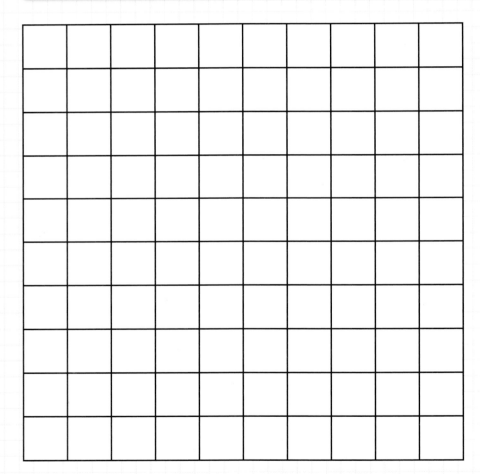

I drew _____ dollar signs.

I need _____ more to make 100.

| Open Number Line | Equation |
|---|---|
|  |  |

**Home Note:** Your child solves a part-part-whole subtraction problem by doing an activity.

# How Many More Dollars to Get to $100?

**1**

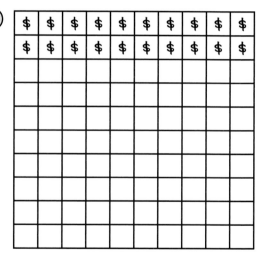

Money saved __$11__

Write money saved.
Each $ is $1 saved.

**2**

+9    +80

11  20        100

or

−9    −80

11  20        100

Draw an open number
line to figure out how
much to get to $100.

**3**

$11 + \underline{89} = 100$

or

$100 - \underline{89} = 11$

Write an equation.

**4**

Money needed to
get to $100  __$89__

Write how much
to get to $100.

---

**①**

| $ | $ | $ | $ | $ | $ | $ | $ | $ | $ |
| $ | $ | $ | $ | $ | $ | $ | $ | $ | $ |
|   |   |   |   |   |   |   |   |   |   |

Money saved _____

Open number line

Equation _____

**Money needed to get to $100** _____

**②**

| $ | $ | $ | $ | $ | $ | $ | $ | $ | $ |
| $ | $ | $ | $ | $ | $ | $ | $ | $ | $ |
| $ | $ | $ | $ | $ | $ | $ | $ | $ | $ |
| $ | $ | $ | $ | $ | $ | $ | $ | $ | $ |
| $ | $ | $ | $ | $ | $ | $ | $ |   |   |

Money saved _____

Open number line

Equation _____

**Money needed to get to $100** _____

---

**Home Note:** Your child solves a part-part-whole subtraction problem by doing an activity.

**(3)**

Money saved _____

Open number line

Equation _____

**Money needed to get to $100** _____

**(4)**

Money saved _____

Open number line

Equation _____

**Money needed to get to $100** _____

**(5)**

Money saved _____

Open number line

Equation _____

**Money needed to get to $100** _____

**(6)**

Money saved _____

Open number line

Equation _____

**Money needed to get to $100** _____

Lesson 22

 **Home Note:** Your child solves part-part-whole subtraction problems when the whole is 100.

# Puzzle Grids

**1**

Circle the numbers with a sum of 100.

**2**

| 25 | 50 |
|----|----|
| 50 | 75 |

Write the missing number to make a sum of 100. Circle the pair.

---

① 
| 50 | 99 |
|----|----|
|    | 50 |

② 
| 80 | 70 |
|----|----|
| 20 |    |

③ 
| 36 | 81 |
|----|----|
|    | 64 |

④ 
| 25 | 61 |
|----|----|
| 39 |    |

⑤ 
| 30 | 21 |
|----|----|
|    | 70 |

⑥ 
| 42 | 22 |
|----|----|
| 78 |    |

⑦ 
| 51 | 45 |
|----|----|
| 49 |    |

⑧ 
| 16 |    |
|----|----|
| 74 | 84 |

⑨ 
|    | 28 |
|----|----|
| 69 | 31 |

➤ Circle each pair of numbers with a sum of 100.

⑩ 
| 80 | 35 | 42 | 58 |
|----|----|----|----|
| 20 | 91 | 65 | 75 |
| 33 | 9  | 10 | 25 |
| 67 | 96 | 4  | 90 |

**Home Note:** Your child identifies pairs of numbers with sums of 100 on puzzle grids.

# How Many More?

| 1 | 2 | 3 | 4 |
|---|---|---|---|
| Kris has **23** cherry tomatoes. She needs **52** for her recipe. How many more does she need? Read the problem. | $+7$ $+20$ $+2$ 23 30 50 52 $23 + 29 = 52$ Draw an addition open number line. Write the equation. | $-7$ $-20$ $-2$ 23 30 50 52 $52 - 29 = 23$ Draw a subtraction open number line. Write the equation. | ___29___ Write the answer. |

| Problem | Addition Open Number Line and Equation | Subtraction Open Number Line and Equation |
|---|---|---|
| ① Tyler planted **57** seeds. He wants **95** plants in all. How many more does he have to plant? ___46___ | $51 + 46 = 95$ | 5 |
| ② Sharol saved **$14**. She needs **$85**. How much more does she need to save? _____ | | |
| ③ Jorge has **49** buttons. He needs **82** for an art project. How many more does he need? _____ | | |
| ④ Darrell read **13** pages. There are **69** pages in all. How many more pages does he have to read? _____ | | |

**Home Note:** Your child solves part-part-whole subtraction problems in which the whole is not 100.

# Show What You Know

➤ Read the problem.

➤ Draw an addition open number line. Write the equation.

➤ Draw a subtraction open number line. Write the equation.

➤ Write the answer.

| Problem | Addition Open Number Line and Equation | Subtraction Open Number Line and Equation |
|---|---|---|
| ① Tom has written 45 invitations so far. He needs to write 100 in all. How many more does he need to write? _____ | | |
| ② I made 26 muffins. Then I made some more. Now I have 54 muffins. How many more did I make? _____ | | |
| ③ Our class raised $65. We need $100 in all. How much more do we need? _____ | | |
| ④ I read 47 pages. There are 95 pages in all. How many more pages do I need to read? _____ | | |

**Home Note:** Your child solves part-part-whole subtraction problems by drawing open number lines.

# Get Close to Zero with Two Cubes

| Roll | Two-Digit Number | Open Number Line | Equation |
|------|------------------|------------------|----------|
| **EXAMPLE** 5 / 1 | 51 | −1 −50 <br> 49 50      100 | $100 - 51 = 49$ |
| ① ___ ___ | | | |
| ② ___ ___ | | | |
| ③ ___ ___ | | | |
| ④ ___ ___ | | | |
| ⑤ ___ ___ | | | |
| ⑥ ___ ___ | | | |
| ⑦ ___ ___ | | | |
| ⑧ ___ ___ | | | |

**Home Note:** Your child practices subtracting two-digit numbers by playing a game.

# Three Ways to Subtract

| SAMPLE PROBLEM | |
|---|---|
| ① Janelle saved $62. Her sister Marisol saved $41. What is the difference between the amounts the girls saved? _____ | Find the distance from 62 to 41. |
| | Find the distance from 41 to 62. |
| | Take away 41 from 62. |

## DIRECTIONS

➤ Choose one way to solve each problem with an open number line.

➤ Write an equation for each problem.

➤ Write the answer.

| | |
|---|---|
| ② Alex's grandmother gave him 75¢. He spent 47¢. How many cents does he have left? _____ | Open Number Line<br><br>Equation |
| ③ My dog weighs 42 pounds. My friend's dog weighs 28 pounds. What is the difference of their weights? _____ | Open Number Line<br><br>Equation |
| ④ My mother baked 40 cookies. My friends and I ate 24 of them. How many cookies are left? _____ | Open Number Line<br><br>Equation |
| ⑤ The final score of a basketball game was 83 to 57. What was the difference of the scores? _____ | Open Number Line<br><br>Equation |

**Home Note:** Your child chooses one of three ways to solve subtraction problems.

# Game Rules for More or Less Than 40

### What you need

- number cube (1–6)
- number cube (4–9)
- *WorkSpace* page 53

➤ **Player A gets 1 point when a difference is *greater than* 40.**

➤ **Player B gets 1 point when a difference is *less than* 40.**

➤ **Both players get 1 point when a difference *equals* 40.**

**1**

**Player A**              **Player B**

Each player rolls the number cubes, makes a
two-digit number, and secretly records the number.

**2**

| Round | My Number | Partner's Number | Open Number Line | Player A Point | Player B Point |
|-------|-----------|------------------|------------------|----------------|----------------|
| 1 | 29 | 73 |  −6  −3  −20<br>44  50  53     73 | 1 | |

Players show their numbers.

They both draw an open number line to figure out the
difference between the numbers, and mark the score.

➤ **The winner is the player with more points after four
rounds. If the game is tied, players play one more round.**

**Home Note:** Your child practices figuring out differences
between two-digit numbers by playing a game.

# More or Less Than 40

| Round | My Number | Partner's Number | Open Number Line | Player A Point | Player B Point |
|---|---|---|---|---|---|
| EXAMPLE | 37 | 84 | −3  −4  −40<br>37  40  44      84 | 1 | |
| ① | | | | | |
| ② | | | | | |
| ③ | | | | | |
| ④ | | | | | |
| Tie-Breaker | | | | | |
| Total Points | | | | | |

**Home Note:** Your child practices figuring out differences of two-digit numbers by playing a game.

# High and Low Temperatures in January

DIRECTIONS

➤ Find the difference between each city's high and low temperatures.

| High and Low Temperatures for a Day in January (°F) | | | |
| City | High Temperature | Low Temperature | Difference |
| --- | --- | --- | --- |
| Anchorage | 25 | 18 | |
| Atlanta | 50 | 36 | |
| Chicago | 40 | 29 | |
| Cleveland | 40 | 30 | |
| Denver | 64 | 27 | |
| Little Rock | 63 | 45 | |
| New York City | 43 | 34 | |
| New Orleans | 60 | 46 | |
| Oklahoma City | 76 | 42 | |
| Omaha | 52 | 30 | |
| Philadelphia | 38 | 28 | |
| San Francisco | 56 | 49 | |
| St. Louis | 51 | 40 | |
| Tucson | 82 | 54 | |

**Home Note:** Your child figures out the differences between cities' high and low temperatures.

# Temperature Problems

DIRECTIONS

**1**
Denver had a low temperature of 27°F.

Cleveland had a low temperature of 30°F.

How much colder was Denver?

Read the problem.

**2**
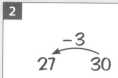

Draw an open number line.

**4**
3

Write the answer.

| Problem | Open Number Line | Answer |
|---|---|---|
| **1** San Francisco had a high temperature of 56°F.<br><br>New York City had a high temperature of 43°F.<br><br>How much warmer was San Francisco than New York City? | | |
| **2** Omaha had a low temperature of 30°F.<br><br>Anchorage had a low temperature of 18°F.<br><br>How much colder was Anchorage than Omaha? | | |
| **3** Tucson had a high temperature of 82°F.<br><br>Philadelphia had a high temperature of 38°F.<br><br>How much warmer was Tucson than Philadelphia? | | |

**Home Note:** Your child uses subtraction to compare cities' temperatures.

# High and Low Temperatures in June

➤ Find the difference between each city's high and low temperatures.

| City | High Temperature | Low Temperature | Difference |
|------|------------------|-----------------|------------|
| Anchorage | 83 | 52 | |
| Atlanta | 76 | 67 | |
| Chicago | 96 | 72 | |
| Cleveland | 81 | 68 | |
| Denver | 84 | 59 | |
| Little Rock | 94 | 68 | |
| New York City | 89 | 70 | |
| New Orleans | 85 | 66 | |
| Oklahoma City | 88 | 65 | |
| Omaha | 93 | 74 | |
| Philadelphia | 76 | 67 | |
| San Francisco | 63 | 55 | |
| St. Louis | 95 | 71 | |
| Tucson | 104 | 78 | |

**High and Low Temperatures for a Day in June (°F)**

**Home Note:** Your child figures out the differences of cities' high and low temperatures.

# Write About Subtraction

➤ Tell about subtraction with words, numbers, and pictures.

**ABOUT SUBTRACTION**

# Running Speed of Land Animals

| Running Speed of Land Animals (miles per hour) | |
|---|---|
| **Animal** | **Speed** |
| Cheetah | 70 |
| Antelope | 60 |
| Lion | 53 |
| Coyote | 45 |
| Hyena | 39 |
| Rabbit | 35 |
| Giraffe | 32 |
| Grizzly Bear | 29 |
| Elephant | 25 |
| Wild Turkey | 15 |
| Squirrel | 12 |
| Spider | 1 |

**Home Note:** Your child studies animals' speeds.

# Problems About Speeds of Land Animals

**DIRECTIONS**

➤ Use the table *Running Speed of Land Animals* on page 58.

➤ Draw an open number line for each problem.

➤ Write the difference of the speeds of the animals.

**1** Compare the speeds of the antelope and the elephant.

| Animal Speeds | Open Number Line | Difference |
|---|---|---|
| | | |

**2** How much slower is the wild turkey than the rabbit?

| Animal Speeds | Open Number Line | Difference |
|---|---|---|
| | | |

**3** Write your own problem about two animals' speeds.

_____

_____

_____

| Animal Speeds | Open Number Line | Difference |
|---|---|---|
| | | |

**Home Note:** Your child uses subtraction to compare animals' speeds.

**Lesson 30**

**59**

# Show What You Know

➤ Use the table to solve the problems.

➤ Draw an open number line for each problem.

| Speed of Animals (miles per hour) | | | | | |
|---|---|---|---|---|---|
| Runners | | Swimmers | | Flyers | |
| Cheetah | 70 | Sailfish | 68 | Peregrine falcon | 200 |
| Antelope | 60 | Marlin | 50 | Spin-tail Swift | 106 |
| Lion | 53 | Bluefin Tuna | 46 | Frigate Bird | 96 |
| Coyote | 45 | Blue Shark | 43 | Swan | 56 |
| Zebra | 40 | Killer Whale | 34 | Duck | 53 |
| Hyena | 39 | Sea Lion | 25 | Pheasant | 37 |

1. What is the difference between the speeds of the cheetah and the killer whale? _____

2. What is the difference between the speeds of the lion and the sea lion? _____

3. What is the difference between the speeds of the swan and the coyote? _____

4. Choose two animals and write their names below.

_____     _____

What is the difference between the speeds of your animals? _____

**Home Note:** Your child uses subtraction to compare animals' speeds.

# Math Vocabulary

➤ Write new words and terms in the box.

➤ Write a definition, show an example, or draw a picture for each word or term in your list.

**Home Note:** Your child records terms and examples of math vocabulary.

# Math Vocabulary

➤ Write new words and terms in the box.

➤ Write a definition, show an example, or draw a picture for each word or term in your list.

**Math Vocabulary**

**Home Note:** Your child records terms and examples of math vocabulary.

# Glossary

## add

*Add* is what you do to find the total number when two or more sets are combined. To *add* means to combine two numbers to find out how many there are in all. The plus symbol + tells you to add.

## addend

In the equation $4 + 2 = 6$, the two numbers being added are called *addends*. 4 and 2 are *addends*; 6 is the sum. There may be many *addends*. In $1 + 2 + 3 + 4 = 10$, 1, 2, 3, and 4 are all *addends*.

## addition

*Addition* is used to tell how many things there are when two sets are combined. The plus symbol + tells you to add.

## addition equation

An *addition equation* is a number sentence that has two sides separated by an equal sign. Both sides have the same value and there is addition on one or both sides. Examples of addition equations are $4 + 2 = 6$, $4 + 2 = 3 + 3$, and $9 = 7 + 2$.

## comparing problem

In a *comparing problem*, you know two amounts and you figure out the difference between them.

For example, you have $20 and your sister has $30. What is the difference between the two amounts?

## difference

The answer to a subtraction problem is called the difference. For $5 - 3 = 2$, we say the difference between 5 and 3 is 2.

## digit

In a number, the numerals 0 to 9 are called *digits*. In 258 the digits are 2, 5, and 8. 258 is a three-digit number because there are three digits.

## equal

*Equal* means the same amount. For example, seven is *equal* to four plus three. The symbol for equal is $=$.

## equation

An *equation* is a number sentence that has an equal sign to show that two amounts have the same value. For example, $3 + 4 = 7$ is an *equation*.

## minus

The minus sign tells us to subtract. For $5 - 3 = 2$ we say 5 minus 3 equals 2.

## multiples of ten

When you start with 10 and count by tens, the numbers you get are called *multiples of 10*.

10, 20, 30, 40, 50, . . . are *multiples of ten*.

We say 20 is a *multiple of 10* because it is a number you get when counting by tens.

# Glossary

## open number line

An *open number line* is a visual model that is like a number line but the only numbers you see are the ones you write for that particular problem. The open number line is a tool you will use to solve addition and subtraction problems.

Here is an example of an open number line for $10 - 7$.

$$\overset{-7}{3 \curvearrowleft 10}$$

## part-part-whole

In a *part-part-whole problem*, if you know one of the parts and you know the whole, you can find the other part by adding or subtracting.

For example, $3 + \underline{\hspace{1cm}} = 7$; the known part is 3 and the total is 7. You can subtract $7 - 3$ to find the missing part or you can say *3 plus what number is 7* to answer it.

## plus

The word *plus* tells you to add. *3 plus 3* means you should add $3 + 3$. The symbol for plus is $+$.

## subtract

*Subtract* is what you do when you solve a subtraction problem such as $5 - 3$.

## subtraction

*Subtraction* is what you do when you subtract. We can show subtraction with a subtraction equation such as $5 - 3 = 2$.

## subtraction equation

A *subtraction equation* is a number sentence that has two sides separated by an equal sign. Both sides have the same value and there is subtraction on one or both sides. An example of a subtraction equation is $7 - 3 = 4$.

## sum

The *sum* is the answer you get when you add two or more numbers. In the addition equation $2 + 3 + 5 = 10$, 10 is the *sum*.

We can ask the question, *What is the sum of 2 and 3?* This is the same as saying, *What is 2 plus 3?*

## symbols

You use *symbols* in mathematics to name numbers (12, 308, $\frac{1}{2}$), operations ($+$, $-$, $\times$, $\div$), and relationships between numbers ($=$, $>$, $<$).

## take-away

In a *take-away problem*, you know the starting amount and you know how much was taken away, and you figure out how much is left by subtracting.

For example, you had $50 and you spent $20. How much money is left?